Teachers Pick their Noses

and other poems

Teachers Pick their Noses

and other poems

By Conrad Burdekin

Illustrations by Lilian Fitchett

Published by Olive Tree Books

First Published 2012

Olive Tree Books, Wakefield, UK.

Text ©2012 Conrad Burdekin
Illustrations ©2012 Lilian Fitchett

www.conradburdekin.com

Printed by
Beamreach Printing (www.beamreachuk.co.uk)

ISBN 978-0-9565863-1-5

To Clare,

without whom my books would not exist.

Contents

All About Who?

Bonkers as a barmy bat
Silly as a circus cat
Crazy as a caterpillar
Cheeky as a pet chinchilla
Dozy as a dozing dog
Foolish as a flying frog
Wacky as a wallaroo
Kooky as a Kangaroo
Loopy as a ladybird
Eating ice-cream – how absurd!
Potty as a parakeet
Freaky as a fish with feet
Dippy as a dinosaur
Louder than a lion's roar
Nutty as a nanny goat
Eating hats and winter coats
Can you guess it? Don't you see?
This poem is all about Me! Me! Me!

The Beastly Bunch

Ready, steady, it's Earwax Eddy
Pulling out yellow chunks of gunk
Here she goes, it's Bogey Rose
Picking out green slimy junk
How unreal, it's Belly Button Neil
Digging deep for stinky fluff
Well I never, it's Toenail Trevor
Eating filthy nails and stuff
What a to-do, it's Spotty Sue
Bursting spots right on her chin
Oh my gosh, it's Junk Food Josh
Stuffing chips and pizzas in
What a man it's Dandruff Dan
Shaking flakes all over town
Thank the Lord, they've gone abroad
And left me in my dressing gown!

Peas

I will not eat those yucky peas
Not even if you say, 'Oh, please'
Not even if you scream and shout
Not even if you dance about

I will not eat them even if
I have to sit with legs gone stiff
I will not eat them hot or cold
I will not eat them when I'm old

I will not put a single one
Inside my mouth or in my tum
And if you tell me there's no pud
I'll fold my arms and bellow, "Good!"

So let's see who will win this war
I've won the ones that came before
I'll win this too, just wait and see
For I will NEVER eat a pea!

Bogey Glue

Achoo! Achoo!
We're making Bogey Glue

Pull it out of your big nose
Wipe it on your sister's clothes
Stick it in your teacher's hair
Smear it underneath your chair

Achoo! Achoo!
We're making Bogey Glue

Splodge it on your daddy's head
Flick it on your mummy's bed
Squish it in your brother's lunch
Eat it with a munch! munch! munch!

Achoo! Achoo!
We're making Bogey Glue

Stash it behind your left ear
Leave it there for years and years
Frame it on the fireplace
Spread it on your best friend's face

Achoo! Achoo!
We're making Bogey Glue

Would you
Would you
Would you
Would you
Would you like to make some too?

AAAAAAAchoo!

Gorgeous Granny

Gorgeous Granny
Lucky me
My best friend
For all to see

Wrinkled face
Sparkly eyes
Tells tall stories
Gives high fives

Knobbly knees
Jumps in puddles
Loses keys
Likes big cuddles

Gnarled up fingers
Painted toes
Can't stand winter
Wears posh clothes

Munches chocolate
Eats dry bread
Girly giggles
Hair dyed red

Drives too fast
Cries at songs
Makes me happy
All day long

Gorgeous Granny
Lucky me
My best friend
For all to see

The Footballer

Tackles hard
Wears shin guards
Corner taker

Play maker
Free kick blaster
Dribbling master

Fast runner
Scores stunners
Crowd pleaser

Defence teaser
Picks a pass

Pure class
With a ball
He's King of all

Captain Cut-throat

Captain Cut-throat sails the seas
Filthy beard full of fleas
Mouth a wicked, evil sneer
He's the pirate people fear.

Captain Cut-throat sails the seas
Clothed in sickness and disease
Putrid warts stick to his skin
Pus-filled sores burst on his chin.

Captain Cut-throat sails the seas
Crooked back and knobbly knees
Teeth turned black and falling out
Feet dark green with rotten gout.

Captain Cut-throat sails the seas
Stinky feet of mouldy cheese
Dirty, sweaty, scabby toes
Creatures crawling up his nose.

Captain Cut-throat sails the seas
Never says thank you, never says please
Shouts at shipmates, whips them too,
Hated by his villainous crew.

Captain Cut-throat sailed the seas
Crafty pirates stole his keys
Locked him up and sank the boat
Poor old Captain Cut-throat.

Teachers pick their noses

Teachers pick their noses
With fingers long as garden hoses
Reaching up and in they go
They dig real deep, they dig real slow.

"Aha!" yells Mr Barry,
In the staffroom by the sink
"I've picked a winner, this one's great,
What do you lot think?"

He holds the bogey in the air,
A smile on his face
"Just look at it!" he shouts out loud.
"A bright green one – it's ace!"

Mrs Smith stands to her feet:
"I'll beat that, wait and see."
And with her little finger
She begins to pick with glee.

With ultra concentration
She scrapes and tugs and pulls
Until a moment later
She's got a finger-full!

"Slimy ones, sixteen at least,"
She laughs with utmost pleasure
"Now that's what I call truly great
Bogey-picking treasure."

And after showing off her prize
She sends the bogey south
Sliding off her finger
Straight into her mouth.

Mr Jones finds dried up crusties
Stuck inside his nose
And of Miss Brook, the Year Two teacher,
What do you suppose?

She rams both thumbs inside her nostrils,
Then (and this is grim!),
She pulls out huge big greenies
And sticks them to her chin.

The bogey-picking gets more frenzied
Led by Year Four's Miss McKenzie
Who with a look of sheer delight
Begins a teacher's bogey fight.

She flicks a round one through the air
It lands in Mr Smalling's hair
He retaliates, of course
But by mistake hits Mrs Morse.

And now the rest of them join in
"This sure beats teaching," they all sing
Their only aim – to pick and flick –
They're super fast, they're super quick!

Bogeys whizz across the room
They soar! They sail! They whizz! They zoom!
The teachers laugh and scream and squeal
Full of bogey-throwing zeal.

Until, that is, the staffroom door
Reveals the frightening Mrs Moore
Headteacher with a fearsome face
She looks around and roars: "Disgrace!"

The teachers gulp, the teachers shake
Their laughter stops, their bodies quake
"We're sorry, Miss," they say as one
"We meant it as a bit of fun."

They're desperate for their Mighty Chief,
To offer signs of some relief.
And so they pick up all the snot
On hands and knees they find the lot.

"Oh stop!" the Head cries, "I agree.
In fact I often feel the need
To have a good old dig myself
Ten minutes a day improves my health.

But next time do not dare to start
Before you ask me to take part
Now watch and learn, you lousy bunch
(Though this might put you off your lunch)."

She shoves her fingers up her snout
"Just wait, you guys, there's more," she shouts
Before long her whole arm's up there
Deep into the bogey lair.

But Mrs Moore is not done yet
Her forehead glistens with her sweat
She then unveils a ghastly grin
And stabs her arm up, further in.

The teachers hardly dare to look
With awe they wonder what she's hooked
Upon her fingers, in her hand –
The greatest bogey in the land?

Eventually her arm's back out
The colour now of Christmas sprouts
And with a stifled cry of pain
Within her hand, she holds – HER BRAIN!

Mr Jones falls off his chair
Miss Brook pulls out all her hair
Mrs Morse faints to the floor
Mr Barry dives next door.

Through the windows others go
Off to where? I do not know
But after that, the children come
To see what's made the teachers run.

And when they see, they start to shriek
And gasp and cry and howl and squeak
Good job that Mrs Moore is cool
The calmest person in the school.

She slowly starts to push her brain
Back up into her head again
And when it's fixed quite firm and tight
She says, "I'm sorry, for the fright.

I didn't mean to get my brain
I must have been a bit off aim.
It sometimes happens when you pick
I'm sorry if I've made you sick."

All of which just goes to show,
You must not pick your nose you know!
For you'll get bogeys in the main
But one day you might pick your brain!

Grumpy Santa

"Come on," ordered Santa
"I need help, Mr Elf."
"I can't," he replied,
"I'm not quite myself.

I'm hot and I'm sweaty
I don't feel the tops
And besides all of that
I'm covered in spots."

"Right," shouted Santa,
"That's it then, you're fired!
I'm too old for this
Too fat, and too tired."

So poor Mr Elf
Has no job anymore
Since grumpy old Santa
Showed him the door!

My shadow

My shadow is annoying me
He's sticking to my feet
On the pavement, on the grass,
All along the street.

I jump up high but he stays calm
And waits until I land
Wherever I decide to go
That's where my shadow stands.

And then a cloud! The sun has gone!
I hear a sudden cry
At last my shadow is no more
Good riddance and Goodbye!

My Silly Daddy (the return!)

He shouts and screams at football teams
When they are on the telly
He does not change his pants for days
Until they're ultra smelly.

He takes me to the local zoo
Then acts like he's a monkey
He picks his nose and wears strange clothes
And thinks he's cool and funky.

He fills our bath with Heinz Baked Beans
And dives in with a splat
He eats a dish of stinky fish
And meows like a cat!

He sings for hours in the shower
Whilst he cleans his hair
He crawls around and makes strange sounds
Pretending he's a bear.

He fills mum's shoes with slimy goo
And pours some in her hat
He goes to bed stood on his head
And says that he's a bat.

He reads me tales of purple whales
And sharks who do ballet
And then he jumps from my top bunk
And cackles, "Bombs away!"

I love my silly daddy
I'm sure that you can see
But more than that (this is a fact)
I know that he loves me.

My daughter Alice

If you count her in years she's just over one
If you count her in months she's almost fourteen
If you count her in weeks she's exactly sixty
If you count her in days she's four hundred and twenty one
If you count her in hours she's more than ten thousand
If you count her in minutes she's past half a million
If you count her in seconds she's..........lots!

If you count her in mornings she's a bird's first song
If you count her in smiles she's a room lighting up
If you count her in giggles she's a belly fit to burst
If you count her in cuddles she's a squeeze of delight
If you count her in baths she's a bubble and a SPLASH!
If you count her in sleep she's a pyjama-ful of dreams
If you count her in cute she's a dimple in her cheek
If you count her in love she's my whole heart.

Colds

Bunged up with bogies
I can't breathe
Tissues, hankies
Sniff! Sniff! Sneeze!

Snot-filled nostrils
Head full of pain
Another stinking cold
Not again!

I'm fed up
Big bad mood
My throat hurts
Can't taste food

No school for me
Not today
'Till mum says
"You'll be ok."

Grumble, moan
Sniff! Sniff! Achoo!
I hate colds
Boo! Hoo! Hoo!

Cricket Wish

Cricket should be played at school
From nine until half three
At least that's what would happen
If the choice were left to me
The teachers would be padded up
Ready for a match
The pupils all around the bat
Waiting for a catch
I bet we'd beat them – Yes! We would!
I'd smack a massive six
We'd laugh as teachers blubbed and cried
And moaned: "This game's a fix!"
The watching crowds would gasp and cheer
"Amazing! What a ball!"
And when the winter clouds brought snow
We'd move into the hall
"Good day?" my mum and dad would ask
"Did you have any luck?"
"I won the headteacher's award," I'd say,
"Then bowled him for a duck."

Ride a cock horse

Rice a cock horse to Banburry Cross
To see a fine lady upon a white horse
She shall have music wherever she goes
For she has got tambourines stuck up her nose

Hey diddle diddle

Hey diddle diddle, the cat and the fiddle
The cow jumped over the moon
"That's quite enough," his mother yelled
"It's bath and bedtime soon."

Little Miss Muffet

Little Miss Muffet sat on a tuffet
Eating a bag of sweets
Along came her sister, who scoffed them and whispered
"Tell mum, and you'll be dead meat!"

Mary Mary

Mary, Mary, quite contrary
In her garden met a fairy
Said the fairy to our Mary
"Goodness me – your legs are hairy!"

Pussycat, Pussycat

Pussycat, pussycat, where have you been?
I've been to London to visit the Queen
Pussycat, pussycat, what did you there?
I knocked off her crown and cut off her hair

Humpty Dumpty

Humpty Dumpty stood on a wall
Never before had he felt so tall
When all of a sudden he tripped and fell
Broke both his arms and shattered his shell

Mary had a little lamb

Mary had a little lamb
She also had a fox
The two of them did not get on
And stole each other's socks

I'm a Yorkshire teapot

I'm a Yorkshire teapot short and stout
Tip me up I'll give you nowt
Tea's too pricey, coffee's yuck
Guess that means you're out of luck

Wee Willie Winkie

Wee Willie Winkie running through the town
Upstairs, downstairs in his nightgown
Mum got cross, her face bright red,
Sent him straight upstairs to bed

Sam, Sam, the Sandwich Man

Sam, Sam, the Sandwich Man
Puts rice crispies with his jam
Does not have much chocolate spread
Uses slugs and snails instead
Squirts on loads of Mayonnaise
Looks like he'll be ill for days!

Cheating Tortoise

There once was a tortoise called Sid
Who loved all the sports that he did
But one day he cheated
And often repeated
So we sold him up town for a quid

Cross-Country Runner

His feet race across sodden fields
Legs splashed with mud
Shorts flapping against bare legs
Tongue hanging out of his mouth
As he pants like a thirsty dog on a summer's day.
Peering into the gloomy distance
He prays for the finish line
Wishing that he'd been a sprinter
How he hates cross country in winter.

Sleepy Sue

Sleepy Sue, oh Sleepy Sue
She stays in bed till half past two
She sleeps past breakfast, snores through lunch
She's far too tired to even munch

A boiled egg, some beans on toast
A slice of ham or Sunday roast
And when she does get out of bed
The sleepiness stays in her head.

She yawns her way downstairs at three
No school for Sue, no literacy
No lining up, no register
No spelling test or maths for her.

By tea time Sue is quite unable
To stay conscious at the table
She falls headfirst into her food
Mum rolls her eyes, Dad says, "How rude!"

And nothing that I do or say
Appears to matter either way
In fact, last week I called at Sue's
To give her some exciting news.

Two doctors (who I think were Greek)
Had found a cure for too much sleep
I'd bought a jar of their new stuff
The advert said it was enough

To sort the deepest sleeper out
It could not fail, there was no doubt
I rushed upstairs to poor Sue's bed
Excitement racing through my head.

"I know," I gasped, "what we must do
To stop you being so sleepy, Sue
I've got the cure, I've got the fix
Just drink the lot and gulp this mix."

Sue yawned, then drank the whole jar down
She coughed and burped, she shook and frowned
Then up she leapt out from her bed
"It works," she laughed. "You're healed," I said.

The two of us we danced around
You should have heard our joyful sounds
But then Sue lay down on the floor
And said (with eyes closed), "Shut the door."

It was enough to make me weep
For Sue had gone straight back to sleep
The cure was false, the cure was fake
Sue snored and snored, she would not wake.

I could not wake that Sleepy Sue
I really tried, I promise you
And so she'll stay, forevermore,
Asleep there on her bedroom floor.

A Happy Poem

I'm a happy, hoppy, hippy, skippy
Whippy sort of poem
I'm a razzy, snazzy, disco-jazzy
Tazzy kind of thing
I'm a whooshing, swooshing, starlight-wishing
Swishing type of rhyme
I'm a bingo, bongo, dance-the-congo
Song-o you can sing
Have a look, a read, a glance
A sneaky peak or three
Let my words sink in your skin
Then come and dance with me.

Grumpy poem

This is a grumpy poem
It got out of bed on the wrong side
At the back of the cupboard it hides
It will not come out and shake your hand
All smiles are banned
In the darkness its grumpiness grows
It will not say 'hi' or 'hello'
This poem is black as a thunder cloud
Enjoyment is not allowed
No laughing, no chuckling, no giggling
No dancing, no jiving, no jiggling
This poem refuses to say anymore
BANG!
And slams shut the cupboard door.

Dancing Mrs Walker

The Year Four teacher, Mrs Walker
Not much of a classroom talker
But – my word! – how she could dance
Across the floor she'd leap and prance.

Her body-popping moves were ace
Her head-spins done at dizzy pace
In fact, last week, she spun so fast
We did not think that she would last.

We thought her head would spin right off
Oh how she laughed! Oh how she scoffed!
"You silly kids, I'm brill," she yelled,
"By far the best, can you not tell?"

But then she whizzed right through the floor
And bits of carpet, tiles and more
Went flying up and all around
As she spun further underground.

Her high heeled shoes were last to go
And from the hole a cry of: "Nooooooo!"
And though we searched and scraped and dug
We had to give up with a shrug.

For dancing Mrs Walker was
No more, you see, and all because
She'd tried to dance, and prance and spin
And made a hole, and fell right in!

Mabel Mobbler

Mabel Mobbler
Tummy wobbler
Nappy filler
Orange juice spiller
Finger licker
Nose picker

Night time waker
Big mess maker
Bath time splasher
Sister basher
Banana masher
Carpet dasher
Big smile giver
Full life liver
Chocolate cruncher
Noisy muncher
Greedy gobbler
Mabel Mobbler

Best friends

At school we had to write
About our bestest mate
"Easy," said Tom, "It's Jack."
"Lewis," said Ben, "He's great."

"Emma," said Tilly,
"Rachel," said Beth,
"Liam," said Luke,
"Aidan," said Seth,
"Hannah," said Ruby,
"Jasmine," said Jade,
"Callum," said Connor,
"Kieron," said Wade.

I did not pick Jade or Wade
I didn't think of Beth
I ruled out Luke and Callum
I barely mentioned Seth
Kieron, Jasmine, Ruby, Liam?
No way, they're too silly
And as for Rachel? Not a chance!
And not that awful Tilly
Maybe Connor? That's before
He threw away my shoe
Hannah? Emma? Aidan? NO!
I mean, come on, would you?

Ben's got Lewis, Jack's got Tom,
And so it's plain to see
There's only once choice left to make
I'll be best friends with me!

Dead Fred

What did you say, mum?
You want me to go and see Fred?
Who's Fred?

Fred's dead?
Poor Fred!

Oh, I see.
You want me to buy some bread
And…put it in…the garden shed…
For Fred?!

I thought Fred was dead –
Why would he need bread
If he was dead?
And what is he doing in
Our garden shed?

And mum – why are you shaking your head?

OH!
Why didn't you say so before!
You want me to **GO TO BED?!**

It's got nothing to do with bread
And Fred
In our garden shed
Dead.

Bed, you said,
Bed, bed, bed.

No thanks.

I'm watching TV
Instead.

Park Swings

Swinging so high
My feet touch the sky
I'm going so fast
The clouds let me past
I reach for the stars
I'm up there with Mars
The Moon and the Sun
Come see what I've done
I hold really tight
And zoom to new heights
I'm having a blast
As rockets whizz past
I feel like a King
Whilst sat on my swing
Look here! Look at me!
I'm flying for free!

Caitlyn Cakey-Pants

Caitlyn Cakey-Pants
Liked to sing and liked to dance
But most of all she liked to bake
Enormous, yummy chocolate cakes.

Last year she made her best by far
A cake much bigger than a car
But did she stop? Of course not – no!
She yelled, "Ok, it's time to go

And make a cake much bigger still
Much taller than the tallest hill
Much higher than the moon and Mars
This cake will reach up to the stars!"

She used a swimming pool to mix
The flour, eggs, and chocolate chips
A crane was used to stir it round
And then guess what our Caitlyn found?

No ovens for this job – instead
A dozen dragons, green and red,
Gathered round to help her bake
Her largest ever chocolate cake.

The mixture bubbled, hissed and spat
As by the pool the dragons sat
And breathed their fire through mouth and nose
Watching as the mixture rose...

...and rose and rose right through the roof
I promise you, this is the truth
It surged across the countryside
There was no time to run and hide.

The schools, the shops, and local zoos
Were closed because of Caitlyn's goo
It filled the earth, the oceans too
All down, of course, to you know who!

It climbed up high, it would not cease
"Oh, help!" cried Caitlyn. "Quick! Police!"
By morning time the cake had raced
Above the clouds and into space.

And so the author of this crime
Tried thinking up a plan in time
To put the cake-mix in reverse
To save the world and Universe.

Moments later, up she leapt
"I am a genius," Caitlyn wept
"I will not contemplate defeat
My plan is simple – I must eat!"

And so began the eat-a-thon
Caitlyn scoffed cake all night long
And as the night turned into day
The cake began to go away.

A day passed, then a week went by
And now the cake was not so high
It came right down from outer space
As Caitlyn stuffed her greedy face.

She showed no signs of slowing down
She did not moan, she did not frown
She simply ate, without a break,
The whole entire chocolate cake.

But sadly she had not foreseen
What eating all this cake would mean
For as she ate the final spoon
Her belly burst like a big balloon.

I Hate Peas

One, two, three, four
Try and eat a little more
Five, six, seven, eight
Eat your peas and clean your plate

Eight, seven, six, five
If I do I won't survive
Four, three, two, one
Please don't make me eat them, mum

One, two, three, four
Hide them in the kitchen drawer
Five, six, seven, eight
Peas are things I really hate!

Eight, seven, six, five
Pass my peas to Uncle Clive
Four, three, two, one
Swap them for a chocolate bun!

Hugs

Hugs from my granny are chin spiky,
Finger wrinkly, bone creaky
Hugs from my grandpa are hair ruffly,
Pat-on-the-back-y, pinch my cheeky
Hugs from my dog are extra smelly
Super slobbery, tail waggly
Hugs from my dad are spinny and dizzy,
High up and whizzy, squashy and squeezy
Hugs from my mum are safe-feely
Soft and cuddly, fall asleepy
These ones are my best-of-all-y

Valentine's Day Yuck!

Smooches and kisses
And slobbery smackers
It's now official
Mum and Dad have gone crackers

Slimy wet snogs
And pecks on the cheek
It's grossing me out
They've been like this all week

"I love you, my snuggles,
My snookums," says dad
Mum blushes and I know for sure
They've gone mad

"Pucker up love,"
Dad moves in for the kill
My parents lock lips
I start to feel ill

Flowers for breakfast
Chocolates for tea
Nothing but
Soppy films on the TV

Cards through the door
And fluffy pink teddies
It's putting me right off
My bowlful of shreddies

Huggles and cuddles
Long walks hand in hand
"Where are my real mum and dad?"
I demand

And what do they say
To explain all of this?
"It's Valentine's day
Come here for a kiss!"

Our sofa

I looked down our sofa and what did I find?
A piece of dad's sandwich and chewed bacon rind
The twelve midnight chimes of our grandfather clock
Two coins and a pen top and one smelly sock
A miaow and a scratch – I'd discovered the cat
Munching old mars bars and growing quite fat
I rooted around and found Grandma down there
Chatting to Grandpa whilst combing his hair
My fingers brushed giggles from when I was small
And stories of witches and giants so tall
I touched lots of laughter and some broken dreams
But best by a mile I found chocolate ice-cream!

Moaning Mum

"You like breakfast, you like lunch
You like lots of things to munch
You like scrambled egg on toast
You like sizzling Sunday roasts

You like butter on your bread
You like peppers, green and red
You like hot dogs, you like fries
You like eating large meat pies

So will you tell me
Would you please
Why you won't eat
Mushy peas?

You like cake and you like buns
You like grapes and juicy plums
You like ketchup on your plate
You think Bolognese is great

You like pizza, chips and beans
You like dates and aubergines
You like crispy, battered fish
You like scampi on your dish

So will you tell me,
Would you please
Why you won't eat
Mushy peas?"

Then mum stops and so I say
"I will not eat those peas, no way
I'd rather eat some mouldy cheese
Than forcing down your mushy peas

They're green and slushy, round and fat
They sit there like a bogey-splat
If I scoffed them I would die
Therefore I will not taste or try."

And though mum starts to cough and wheeze
I will not touch my mushy peas
Mum sighs and counts from one to ten
Then chucks them in the bin...again!

The Recycle Monster

I've got a Recycle Monster
Living in my shed
With scratched CDs for eyes
And a cauliflower head

An empty can of tuna
For each of his six ears
Jagged teeth of rusty chains
And broken bicycle gears

Used up batteries for his fingers
Rotten carrot toes
Ripped up Wellies for his legs
A mobile phone type nose

But if you want the monster
To stay inside his shed
Then listen very carefully
To everything that's said

Reduce, Reuse, Recycle
As much as much can be
Because if you choose not to
He could come round for tea

He'll start with dad's old kettle
Washed down with tins of paint
The fridge he'll munch, the TV next,
He won't display restraint

And though he only wants to scoff
Things that can be re-used
It's possible at bedtime
He'll try to eat you too!

A liddle riddle

I shower in stinky, horrible sweat
After work I smell worse than sour milk
I wear a logo around my neck
Am stretchy like elastic
And often as white as a fluffy cloud in the sky
I am a comforter
Living in many different homes –
A drawer
A washing machine
A boot

What am I?

Answer: see page 87

Don't be me!

Be, oh be, oh be, oh be,
Exactly who you want to be
But please do not try to be me
For if you were, then don't you see?
There would be no room left for me!

Loch Ness Stress

Loch Ness Monster Patrick
Was not feeling great
He thought that Hannah in class three
Would be his bestest mate.

But would she heck
Oh not a chance
Her plan was hatched
He'd sing and dance.

She woke him at the crack of dawn
She would not let him stretch or yawn
"Come on!" she yelled, "now start to sing
I'll make you the X-Factor king."

The poor old lad he tried his best
He had to sing without a rest
For Hannah would not let him stop
"Give me more! You need to rock!"

All Pat wanted was to sleep
To dive down in Loch Ness's deep
To shut his eyes and doze and snooze
"No way," cried Hannah, "then you'd lose."

The day arrived, the show began
Contestants grinned and danced and sang
And who'd have guessed it – Pat was brill!
And as he sang – oh what a thrill!

He smiled at Hannah, she at him
They both held hands and prayed he'd win
Said Simon, "well done, that's three yeses
We'll form a group called Pat's Loch–Nesses!"

And soon Patrick became a star
He topped the charts and drove fast cars
His face was always on TV
He met the Queen and drank her tea.

He wore a huge amount of bling
Girls came from miles to hear him sing
He went on week long shopping sprees
A world renowned celebrity.

So if you travel to Loch Ness
Your chance of seeing Pat is less
Than if you fly to Hollywood
Where he now lives, where life is good.

To Violet

My love for you will be…

As loud as a steam train puffing out smoke
As fizzy as a can of effervescent coke
As full as a life of extravagant joy
As happy as a toddler with a brand new toy
As tall as a mountain capped with snow
As beautiful as legends from long ago
As high as a pair of soaring eagles
As deft and as sure as a surgeon's needle
As exciting as a letter that has just been sent
As long as a journey that never ends
As magical as bells on Santa's sleigh
As pure as a child kneeling down to pray
As sweet as the sound of a chick's first cheep
As calm as a deer when she's settling to sleep

As huge as the moon, beaming down at earth
As proud as parents at their baby's birth
As constant as the oceans that never run dry
As bright as stardust in a night filled sky
As crisp and as clear as a winter's morn
As much when you're old as the day you are born.

A Kenning

Crowd entertainer
Frequent complainer
Patient waiter
Umpire hater
Big hitter
Bench sitter
Fervent polisher
Opponent demolisher
Noisy appealer
Run stealer
Ball spinner
Great winner
Glove user
Bad loser
Scoreboard watcher
Howzat?
Gotcha!

What am I?

Answer: A cricketer

Shoelaces

I make a wicked scrambled egg
I ice-skate standing on one leg
I run the fastest, climb the best
I always get full marks in tests
I swing the highest in the park
On holiday I swim with sharks
At tea I always ask for more
On games I have the highest score
I'm just about the best there is
I'm Super Sonic! Billy Whizz!

But there's one thing I cannot do
I simply cannot tie my shoes
I cannot tie my shoes, my shoes
That is the thing I cannot do

I skateboard with my eyes tight shut
Ramp off the roof of Pizza Hut
I tie my tongue around my nose
I play the piano with my toes

I back flip from the garden shed

I ski down mountains on my head

I wrestle mighty killer whales

I walk across a bed of nails

I juggle swords, I swallow fire

"He's the greatest," sings the choir.

But there's one thing I cannot do

I simply cannot tie my shoes

I cannot tie my shoes, my shoes

That is the thing I cannot do

I trampoline up to the stars

I zoom around in racing cars

I score more goals than Real Madrid

I am the most amazing kid

I slide down rainbows, jump on clouds

I'm followed by enormous crowds

I loop the loop, I spin around

I make a million from one pound

I am the icing on the cake

I'm Number One for goodness' sake!

But there's one thing I cannot do
(Oh please don't tell the kids at school)
I cannot tie my shoes, my shoes
That is the thing I cannot do!

Last week my dad
slipped in the mud

Last week my dad slipped in the mud
He landed with a great big thud
His trousers turned from white to brown
His face turned from a smile to frown
He tried to stand and slipped again
And tried and tried and tried and then
He sank his face into the mud
It made a gloopy kind of glug

And when he surfaced, goodness me,
My dad, he shouted, "Wowee Wee!
This mud is great! This mud is fun!"
And so we all began to run
Myself, my mum, my baby bro'
My Uncle Steve and Aunty Jo
My Grandpa Jim, my Nana Pat
We ran and jumped and all fell flat
My Aunty Jo began to laugh
"I think," she said, "we'll need a bath."
And what seemed like forevermore
We squealed and laughed and yelled: "Encore!"
We squidged and squelched and splodged around
A happy, noisy, muddy sound
Our family full of smiles and shrieks
We could have stayed in there for weeks
But then the sun dried up the mud
Which meant that we no longer could
Cavort amidst the sludge and slime
(I guess that all things end sometime)
But dad, just so that you're aware
When you next slip – we'll all be there!

Posh Pat

Our secretary has gone all strange
She's bought a fancy hat
And when folk try to speak to her
She says: "The name's Posh Pat."

"I've got the register," I mumble,
"Should I put it on your desk?"
Her head tilts back, her nose points up,
She stands quite statuesque.

"I simply will not take it, boy,"
She says from way up high.
"No longer shall I bother with
Such trite minutiae.*

My days of classroom registers
And trifling telephone calls
Are soon to be replaced with dancing
At palatial balls.

I'll be regarded as a royal
I'll mix with the elite
And when my driver asks: 'Where to?'
I'll say – The Penthouse Suite."

Posh Pat then sashays through the door
Exquisitely serene
Her final words: "Please tell the Head
I'm orf to see the Queen."

*pronounced: 'my-new-she-eye'

Three Cheers for Mum!

She cooks my tea and runs my bath
She gives me hugs and makes me laugh
She wipes my face and walks me to school
She packs my lunch, she's super cool

She is the undisputed star
Fantastic! Amazing! Best by far
Splendid! Awesome! Number One!
Jump up and down – three cheers for mum!

She sews my socks and cleans my shoes
She helps me find the stuff that I lose
She bakes me buns and irons my clothes
She sometimes lets me pick my nose

She is the undisputed star
Fantastic! Amazing! Best by far
Splendid! Awesome! Number One!
Jump up and down – three cheers for mum!

She boils me eggs with runny yolks
She reads me books and tells me jokes
She always helps me tidy up
She's sure to win the 'Best Mum' Cup!

She is the undisputed star
Fantastic! Amazing! Best by far
Splendid! Awesome! Number One!
Jump up and down – three cheers for mum!

She fixes cuts and poorly knees
She never gives me mushy peas
She cuts my hair and clips my nails
She is the best, she never fails

She is the undisputed star
Fantastic! Amazing! Best by far
Splendid! Awesome! Number One!
Jump up and down – three cheers for mum!

Never Play Football with a Hedgehog

Hedgehog, hedgehog, round the wall
He tackles lion, nicks the ball
He's in their half, he's going well
Tiger's worried, we can tell
He's past the rooster, skins the sheep
He's left the badgers in a heap
This mazy run is quite a sight
Rhino's left the pitch in fright
Still hedgehog runs, he's in the box
And bearing down on 'keeper fox
He lifts his paw – He shoots! He scores!
We raise the roof, we clap, we roar
But now the score stays at one-all
For hedgehog's spikes have popped the ball!

See a penny

See a penny
Pick it up
See a cow pat
Don't get stuck!
See a bogey
Have a lick
See another
EAT IT QUICK!!!

Conrad's stinky sport sock

About the Author

Conrad is a poet, storyteller, and writer, and has visited nearly 100 different primary schools across Yorkshire inspiring children to write. *Teachers Pick their Noses* is his second collection of poems for children. His first – *The Hungrumptious Blumpfh and other poems* – has sold over 2000 copies.

Conrad says that he likes writing poems because they don't take very long and they are allowed to be silly. He is very proud of this book, and especially likes the poem 'Teachers Pick their Noses' which he's had in his head for ages, but which he only wrote down recently. He has no idea where the idea for the poem came from, but maintains that he NEVER picks his own nose (unless there is nobody watching).

To find out more about Conrad, please log on to www.conradburdekin.com where you can hear him read some of his poems, find out what he's been up to, and buy his books.

If you would like Conrad to come and work in your school, you can email him at:

conrad.burdekin@sky.com

Conrad is so excited about this book that yesterday he ran outside in his pyjamas shouting 'Bogeys' at the top of his voice.

Conrad and his girls proving that teachers are not the
only ones who pick their noses…

Acknowldegments

There have been lots of people who have helped in the production of this book. Lilian, you are brilliant! Your illustrations bring so much to my poems. Just promise that in the future you won't stay up till 3am drawing them! David – printer, designer, publishing wizard – a humongous thanks. Without you my books would not look anywhere near so cool. And Clare, I meant what I said in the dedication. Thank you for always believing in me.

A loud 'yippee!' to all the people who give me so many ideas for my poems – whether you mean to or not! To the pupils of All Saints Infant school, *Bogey Glue* is for you. It started life in your school and it was your ideas that formed the bulk of the poem. To mum – yes, *Gorgeous Granny* IS about you. As is *Three Cheers for Mum*. I thought that after my last book it was time I was nice to you. *Sam, Sam, the Sandwich Man* is thanks to you, Steve. It will always remind me of our wacky chats whilst sitting at my kitchen table. *My daughter Alice* is for you, Alice. I know it's four years out of date, but it is very special to me. That poem has been to a LOT of schools, and brought laughter to a LOT of children. *To Violet* is yours, Violet. Strange to think that it was written before I'd ever met you. And, of course, *Mabel Mobbler* is for you, Mabel. Keep smiling your way through life. Thanks also to Pat, secretary at Mapplewell Primary, for giving me the idea for *Posh Pat*. Just promise me you'll never get like that in real life! Miss Walker – *Dancing Mrs Walker* started life at Chesneys when you informed me that you body popped in front of your students!

To Caitlyn at St Michael's Primary, thank you for letting me use your nickname in *Caitlyn Cakey Pants*. It is, without doubt, one of my favourite poems. To the Year 6 class of 2010 at Boothroyd Primary, thanks for your ideas. *Shoelaces* wouldn't have been so much fun without you. And finally, to Hannah at Horbury Bridge J & I – thanks for inspiring *Loch Ness Stress*. I truly love the idea of the Loch Ness Monster winning The X Factor!

Other Poetry Books by
Conrad Burdekin

The Hungrumptious Blumpfh and other poems

www.conradburdekin.com

'The Hand in the Sand' makes me shiver

Grace

I really laughed at your poems. My favourite poem was 'My Silly Daddy', the funniest part was when dad put cornflakes in the kettle

Corey

The story ones are good if they are long. If they are short they are a bit good

George

I like the 'My Mum' one but it is a bit rude

Lauren

Some of these make me laugh a lot

Charlie

Can I just tell you that my son Jack has come home with your book tonight and for the first time ever has sat and wanted to read to me

Jack's mum

I like the ones that are a bit disgusting

William

I laughed so much my head fell off and I had to get tape to stick it back on again

Matthew

Really brilliant, very funny, I loved it

Joseph

I loved the vomit poem, it was disgustingly realistic

Ellie